FART™ PATROL

WHO FARTED?

Bambi Smyth & James Hart

NEVER APPROACH UNARMED!

2.0 "
1.5 "
1.0 "
0.5 "
0 "

BEWARE OF TOXIC FLUIDS

NOT TO BE TRUSTED!

BLASTER

SOUND: *Ba-ba-BOOOOOM!*

SMELL: The bad breath of a grizzly bear, wrestler's sweaty underwear

PERSONALITY: Powerful, bossy, vain

TECHNIQUE: Lifts arms, clenches fists, spins quickly and slams sceptre into the ground

EFFECTS: Knocks humans off feet, makes their eardrums ring, eyeballs sting and noses bleed

TARGETS: School bullies, football players, people who eat too much

RATINGS:
Richter Scale (sound level): ★★★★★
Odor: ★★★☆☆
Human Embarrassment: ★★★★★

SQUIRT

SOUND: *SQUOOoosshhH!*

SMELL: Rotten eggs and the gunky stuff that collects under human toe-nails

PERSONALITY: Makes up for being scrawny by being completely disgusting

TECHNIQUE: Flicks the elastic on his underpants, spins quickly to liquidize gas, then fires away

EFFECTS: Leaves behind a nasty, sticky mess for maximum embarrassment

TARGETS: Babies, toddlers, kids in day-care, school bullies, older people, weightlifters

RATINGS:
Richter Scale (sound level): ★☆☆☆☆
Odor: ★★★★☆
Human Embarrassment: ★★★★★

FLUFF

SOUND: *PHHHhhfffffffff!*

SMELL: Old roses and slightly "off" perfume

PERSONALITY: Girly and sweet-natured. A bit silly and giggles a lot

TECHNIQUE: Closes eyes, swells chest, pouts lips and spins around

EFFECTS: Itchy nose, twitching mouth and severe case of blushing

TARGETS: Mothers, pretty girls, ballet dancers, (but also "tough guys" when she's feeling cheeky)

RATINGS:
Richter Scale (sound level): ★☆☆☆☆
Odor: ★★☆☆☆
Human Embarrassment: ★☆☆☆☆

ED DEAD OR ALIVE!

For being public nuisances

BEWARE: WATER HAZARD

BEWARE OF THE DOG!

LOADED & DANGEROUS

BUBBLES

SOUND: *BbbLUPPpp!*

SMELL: Weird seaweed smell, combined with nice bubble-bath scent

PERSONALITY: Very cheeky and loves playing pranks on humans. Not very smart!

TECHNIQUE: Takes a big breath, dives under water, spins quickly then makes a giant bubble fountain

EFFECTS: Mostly embarrassment, but can soak innocent passers-by

TARGETS: Humans in bathtubs or on the toilet, surfers, lifeguards, people in swimming pools

RATINGS:
Richter Scale (sound level): ★★☆☆☆
Odor: ★☆☆☆☆
Human Embarrassment: ★★☆☆☆

KILLER

SOUND: *Tttsssssssssss*

SMELL: Absolutely disgusting—fresh poo and rotten meat

PERSONALITY: Bad-tempered, stubborn and unpredictable—cute one minute, vicious the next

TECHNIQUE: Bares teeth, spins around chasing tail, then lets one rip

EFFECTS: Fumes make eyes, nose and lips sting, then burns people's throats

TARGETS: Older humans, kids at school who think they're cool, builder's laborers

RATINGS:
Richter Scale (sound level): ★☆☆☆☆
Odor: ★★★★★
Human Embarrassment: ★★★★☆

OOPSIE

SOUND: *WheeeeEEP!*

SMELL: Rotten lemon skin and moldy apples in the bin

PERSONALITY: Shy, friendly, naïve, wants to be friends with everyone

TECHNIQUE: Takes a big breath, runs on the spot, shuts eyes and stamps his feet

EFFECTS: Mild asthma, and surprise at the sudden (and quite loud) sound he makes

TARGETS: Young kids, "goody-goody" pupils at school, strict teachers, the nice "boy next door"

RATINGS:
Richter Scale (sound level): ★★★☆☆
Odor: ★★☆☆☆
Human Embarrassment: ★★★☆☆

Hi there you runts, my name is **BLASTER**,

The Fart Patrol's heroic Master.

I'm bigger, stronger, louder, smarter—

In fact, the whole world's ***GREATEST*** farter!

When any human "beans" appear,

I'll **SNEAK** up on them from the rear

And in an instant, knock them **FLAT**,

And then I'll laugh, and say, "Take that!"

My **EXPLOSiVE** farts can be so great

They cause whole countries to vibrate,

And make the highest mountains rock

Then **CRUMBLE** with the aftershock!

There's nowhere safe for you to hide

(No matter how well fortified),

So if I catch you, be prepared,

To be very, very, very, **SCARED**!

Each time I get the urge to **STRIKE**,

I'll find a human I don't like,

And then, to properly prepare,

I'll take a massive gulp of air,

Then lift my arms and **CLENCH** my fists

And spin around in turns and twists,

Then **BOOOOOOM!** I'll blast like dynamite,

And turn the daytime into night!

I'll **EMBARRASS** the school bully first

(As humans go, they are the worst),

But once I've done my farting stuff,

He won't be feeling quite so tough!

I'll **HiDE** from view at the school sports

And sneak up just behind his shorts,

And **BA-BA-BOOOOOOM!** let off a round

That drops him quickly to the ground.

He'll lie there doubled up in **PAIN**

As if he's been hit by a train,

But all the kids will simply grin

To see the **AWFUL** state he's in—

So pleased to see the tables turned

And law and order be returned.

"Hurrah!" they'll **CHEER**. "It serves you right,

Next time you might be more polite!"

And then I'll pick some football star

(You know how **TOUGH** they think they are!).

And even though he's ten feet tall

I'll wait until he's got the ball,

Then **CLENCH** my fists and start to spin

To help the ritual begin,

And just as he's about to kick,

 I'll play my trick!

The **BLAST** will make his eardrums ring,

And then his eyes begin to **STiNG**,

And next his nose will start to bleed

As my ***REVOLTING*** gas is freed.

"Oh come on, Jack!" his coach will scream.

"That was a **FOUL**—you're off the team!"

But then he too will hit the ground,

As I release another round.

Then fear will spread throughout the crowd

As all the players **SCREAM** out loud,

When I blast off a couple more

With **STINKS** they've never smelt before—

The bad breath of a *GRIZZLY* bear

And wrestler's sweaty underwear.

"Oh *HELP*!" they'll yell. "What will we do?"

As I let off another few.

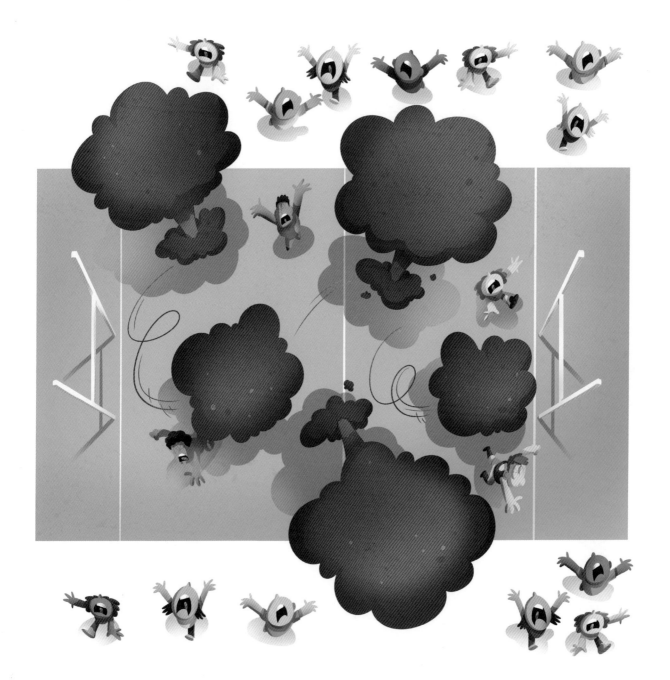

Next up, I'll hit a take-out store

To carry on my toxic war,

And **SNEAK** behind somebody's seat

Who's ordered far too much to eat.

I'll wait until he's **STUFFED** his face

With fries and burgers by the case

Then

BOOOOOOM! I'll go, so loud and foul,

The other diners start to **HOWL**!

Oh yeah, I'm on a lifelong quest
To be the world's most lethal **PEST**,
And blast you stupid human "beans"
Right out of your tight denim jeans.
Not that you'll have the slightest clue
That **DEAFENING** sound was not from you,
But from the Master Blaster, having fun,
'Cause when it comes to **FARTS**, I'm Number One!

Helloooooo humans, **SQUIRT'S** my name

And planting farts is my favorite game,

(Not that I make the usual blend

That make **RUDE** sounds at your rear end,

Or leave a smell so bad you'll choke

And make you think you're going to croak),

But the sort to most embarrass you—

Yep, a fart with **NASTY** follow-through!

You know the sort I mean, I'm sure,

(I'll bet you've done a few before),

The times you **FART**, then get a scare,

When you think you've **POOED** your underwear!

But hey, I've got good news for you,

That's actually **NOT** your poo,

But stuff I've **SQUIRTED** from my nozzle,

(Or, as us Fart Patrollers call it, "snozzle").

Being small and **SCRAWNY** isn't fun,

But I'm not the sort to be outdone,

So it's lucky I've got gas inside

Which I can quickly liquefy,

Until it gets all nice and *GOOEY*

And, to all appearances, "pooey".

So when human "beans" deserve a jolting,

I know how to make them feel *REVOLTING*!

I simply

SQUOOosshhHH!

my contents out

(Into their undies), so they'll shout,

"Uh oh! I've had an accident!"

And **TREMBLE** with embarrassment

And leave the room before it ***STAINS***,

Or someone smells it and complains,

(With none of them about to guess

It was me who'd left the nasty **MESS**!)

It's babies too that get me hyper

When I let **LOOSE** inside their diaper,

Just when a new one's been put on,

And their queasy mother's only gone

Five steps towards the **GARBAGE** bin

To put the stinky old one in.

SQUOOosshhHH!

I'll go, making extra sure

It's even more **DISGUSTING** than before!

"Oh, not again?!" she'll **CROAK**. "I mean,

I've only just got you all clean!"

And back she'll come with her nose *PINCHED*

And pull the waistband out an inch

To see what's going on inside,

(Upon which I will quickly hide,

So that she'll never know it's me

Who's played a *DIRTY* trick—tee hee)!

It's bullies too I like to **FREAK**,

When they pick on kids who are small and meek,

But if in one's pants I can hitch a ride

Then **SQUiRT** my "poo" once I'm inside,

Then he'll have to stand in **MUCK** for hours

(And what it smells of, sure ain't flowers!).

In fact, with undies wet and stained

He'll **STiNK** just like a sewerage drain!

Weightlifters too, are fun to **TRiCK**

So in the gym I'll take my pick,

(But wait a while until I'm sure

I won't get ***STOMPED*** into the floor).

Then as he strains to lift the weights,

(The ones with heavy iron plates),

I'll dive into his stretchy tights

And
SQUOOosshhHH!

I'll go, with all my might!

He'll feel the **HEAT** immediately,

But have no clue that it was me,

So will *BLUSH* deep red and run away.

"I've hurt my back. I'm done," he'll say.

But still the **STiNK** (like dead raccoon)

Will follow him across the room,

And everyone will say, "No, Bert,

More like you've done an undie squirt!"

Oh yeah, I might look small and weak,

But I can make a grown man **SHRiEK**,

By giving him a nasty scare

When I

SQUOOosshhHH!

inside his underwear.

And even kids will get a fright

If I do my **SLOppy** fart just right,

So if you see me creeping past,

You'd better run away—and *FAST*!

Well hello darlings! My name's **FLUFF**

And I love doing sneaky stuff,

Like planting **FARTS** (it's so much fun!)

Then creeping off when I am done.

I do each one most gracefully

And very, very quietly,

To leave a **SMELL** of stale perfume,

Or roses in a stuffy room.

Each time I set about my quest,

I'll close my eyes and swell my chest,

Then pout my lips and start to **SPIN**

To heat up all the gas within.

I'll **TWiRL** about upon my toes

Then wrinkle up my tiny nose,

Then

pHHhhffffffff   I delicately fluff

Like hot breath through a powder-puff.

Sometimes when I'm on **FART PATROL**

I'll find some girls out for a stroll,

And when they ***STOP***, I'll hang around

Till they are seated on the ground.

I'll wait a while before I **SPRiNG,**

To let one loose inside the ring,

Then watch their noses flap and flare

As my ***STRANGE*** perfume fills the air.

"Ooh, who was that?" I'll hear them **WHINE**.

"Don't look at me—it wasn't mine!"

"Was that your fluff?" they each will blame.

"You *DIRTY* girl—aren't you ashamed?"

And on they'll go suspiciously,

Without a clue that it was me,

And as they're **GASPING** for fresh air,

I'll sneak away and leave them there.

I'm very fond of **TEASING** moms

When they're out lunching with their chums,

And acting oh so *LAH-DI-DAH*,

(You know how **POSH** some mothers are!).

I'll sit, all still, beneath their chairs

As up above they talk in pairs,

And then, when they start on dessert

I'll **SNEAK** towards the shortest skirt.

I'll start to spin and gather speed
To help perform my **NAUGHTY** deed,
Then

PHHhhffffff

I'll let a beauty go
And find a perch to watch the show!
For half a tick, no-one will **BUDGE**,
Then one will say, "Please pass the fudge,
And by the way, who let one off?"
As all the others start to **COUGH**.

Their noses will begin to **iTCH**,

And next, their lipsticked mouths will twitch,

Then one will ***BLUSH*** (quite nervously),

And whisper, "Well, it wasn't me."

Her friend snorts, "So who ***IS*** being ***CRASS***?

Real ladies shouldn't let off gas!"

At which, I'll sneak behind her seat

And

PHHhhffffff

let off another treat.

The **SWEAT** will break upon her brow,

As she exclaims, "Hey, come on now,

What's going on? It must be you!

Oh what a **NASTY** thing to do!"

And on they'll go hysterically,

Without a clue that it was me,

And that's when I will take my leave,

Delighted at what I've achieved.

But females aren't the only ones

Who'll feel **EMBARRASSED** when I'm done.

It also can be really great

To tease a trucker with his mates.

PHHhffffff PHHhffffff

I'll go, and twitch my nose,

To fill the air with scent of rose.

"Why do a **GiRLY** fart?" they'll yell.

"If you're going to do it, do it well!"

Oh yes, I really love to tease,

And **TRICKING** humans is such a breeze!

It's fun to make you gasp and **SQUIRM**,

And cause your face and cheeks to burn

When you think it's *YOU* who's done a fluff

But it's Yours Truly, sure enough.

So here's my warning—**STAY ALERT**,

In case I sneak behind your skirt!

FART PATROLLER #4

BUBBLES

THE ONE THAT GETS YOU IN THE WATER!

Hello you guys, it's **BUBBLES** here,

And though at first I may appear

To be quite harmless, don't be caught...

For Fart Patrolling is my sport!

I live in water, swimming free,

But that won't help you **HIDE** from me,

As I'll just **FOLLOW** you around

Whenever you are water-bound.

My bubbly jokes are kind of **FUN**,

And never injure anyone,

But still, I always get a thrill

When I perfect my farting drill.

And though I don't cause actual pain,

EMBARRASSMENT feels much the same,

And once I've **FOOLED** you, I can bet

You'll wish that we had never met!

I find that bath-time is the best
To be an **UNINVITED** guest.
So when I want to make a **FART**,
Up through the plumbing pipes I'll dart
(Without a compass or a map),
Then plop out of the water tap,
And **HIDE** myself beneath the foam
(Where I feel very much at home).

And then when no grown-ups are near,

I'll find a spot by someone's **REAR**,

Then take a breath and dive below

And swim a little, to and fro.

Then

BBLUPP!

I'll let my gases out,

To form a giant water spout,

And make the water froth and bubble

To get my human into **TROUBLE**.

The girls will jump out dripping wet,

Quite clearly shaken and **UPSET**.

"Josh, you're **DISGUSTING**!" they will yell.

"And what's that weird seaweed smell?"

Upon which Josh will go bright red

And **WHIMPER** it was them instead,

And on they'll go, accusingly,

Without a clue that it was me!

Another place I like to **LURK**,

And often do my finest work,

Is when a kid is on the loo

(Especially when they're doing *POO*).

I'll

BBLUPP!

         so loud the bathroom shakes,

To which their Mom says, "Goodness sakes,

What's going on? Are you all right?

That dreadful noise gave me a **FRiGHT**!"

The beach can also be great fun

To get my Fart Patrolling done.

I like the surfboard riders best,

Especially those with **MUSCLY** chests

And arms of steel, all deeply tanned,

Parading up and down the sand,

And trying to **iMPRESS** the girls

With freckled cheeks and sea-tossed curls.

I'll follow one, and breathe right in,

Before I start to quickly **SPiN**

Then

BBLUPP!

I'll let my gases loose

So violently they will produce

A mountain of such froth and bubble

His pal will say, "Uh oh, here's **TROUBLE**,

Although, now that you've made your mark,

I'm glad it scared away that **SHARK**!"

Aquatic ballet shows are best

To put the ladies to the test.

I'll wait until they're **UPSIDE DOWN**

(With their breaths held so they don't drown),

And as they spin about in pairs,

Their legs all graceful in the air,

I'll

BBLUPP!

so hard the pool will ***HEAVE***

And half the audience will leave!

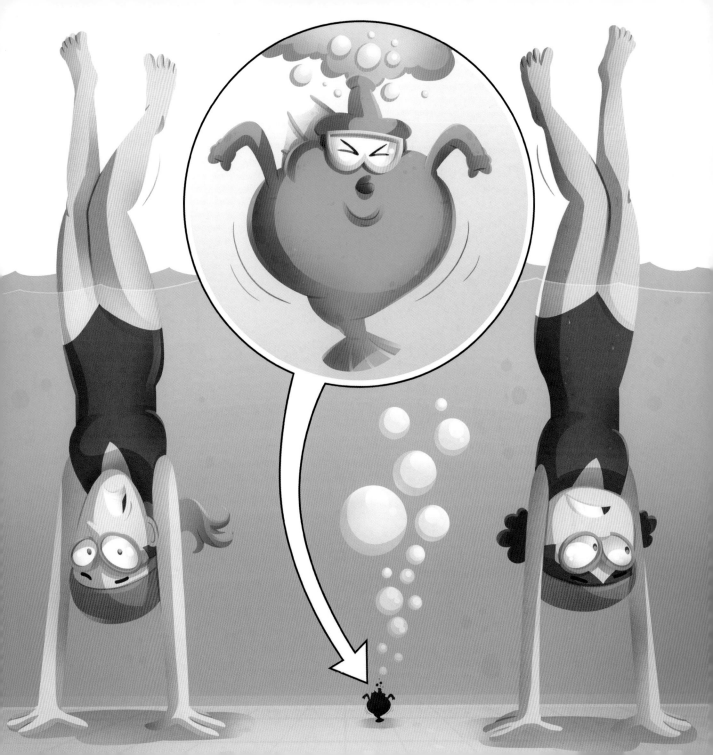

Yes, I just love to make you **JUMP**

When I let loose beneath your rump,

And cause a little "accident"

For maximum embarrassment.

So please remember to ***BEWARE***

When there is water anywhere,

For having **FUN** is what I do

And next time it just might be you!

WATCH OUT you punks, it's **KiLLER** here,

And let me make this very clear:

My one and only aim in life

Is giving dogs and humans **STRIFE**!

I'm fast and **SMART** and really mean

(Most often smelt, but rarely seen),

And what gives me the greatest thrill

Is practising my **FARTiNG** skills.

My farts are so intense they'll **BURN**

Your eyes, then nose, then lips in turn,

And make you **GASP** and scratch your skin

And yell out for some medicine.

In fact, they'll make you feel so ill

You might end up in hospital!

Oh yeah, I am a **VICIOUS** beast

When my foul poisons are released.

Each time I head out on Patrol

(To carry out my **FARTiNG** role),

I'll bare my teeth and spin a lot

To get my gases good and *HOT*.

I'll twirl around till I'm a blur

To help my filthy prank occur,

Then

TttSssssssssssssss I'll let one quietly go,

With fumes so *TOXIC* that they glow!

I'm especially fond of **SNEAKING** up

On someone's unsuspecting pup,

And waiting till I'm nice and close,

Then letting loose a ***WHOPPING*** dose

That stinks of poo and rotten meat

So bad it **POISONS** half the street,

And ***KILLS*** the birds for miles around,

And brings the postman to the ground.

"Oh **YUCK**!" its owner will exclaim

And give his startled pup the blame

As both their nostrils start to stream,

"You **DIRTY** dog!" the man will **SCREAM,**

(Quite clueless that it came from me),

At which the pup will turn and flee,

And **HiDE** behind the garbage bins

Until the fog around them thins.

It's humans too that I attack,

Especially old ones, sitting back

Upon their armchairs, half asleep,

As up behind them I will **CREEP**.

Then  I'll let a **RiPPER** go,

So foul the tears will start to flow.

"Oh hell, Grandpa!" the kids will swear

And **RUN** outside for some fresh air.

I also Fart Patrol at school
And pick the kid who thinks he's **COOL**,
And **CREEP** beneath him as he waits
Inside the canteen with his mates.
But before I pull my **CHEEKY** stunt
I'll hold off till he's near the front,
And hemmed in on at least three sides
Where he can't run away, or hide.

I'll quickly spin into the air,

And

Tttsssssssssssss

I'll let one loose right there,

Of such intense and dreadful **SMELL**

That everyone will start to yell.

"Oh yecch!" they'll shriek, "Was that you, Luke?"

"That was the worst—I'm gonna *PUKE*!"

"You dirty guy! You stink!" they'll shout.

"You're absolutely **GROSS**—get out!"

My target will turn deathly pale,

"It wasn't me, I swear", he'll **WAIL**,

Then watch in ***HORROR*** as his friends

Go on to meet a gruesome end,

And lie there twitching on the floor,

As I go on to do some more.

"It isn't me!" he'll shout in vain,

Before my gases melt his **BRAIN**.

So when you hear of "man's best friend",

That sure ain't me, (so why pretend?).

I mean, your usual cheerful household mutt

Won't give you **RASHES** on your butt.

But it's my job to let you know

It's the **FART PATROL** who run the show.

Yep, there's no mistaking when I've struck,

So if you're in my way— *TOUGH* luck!

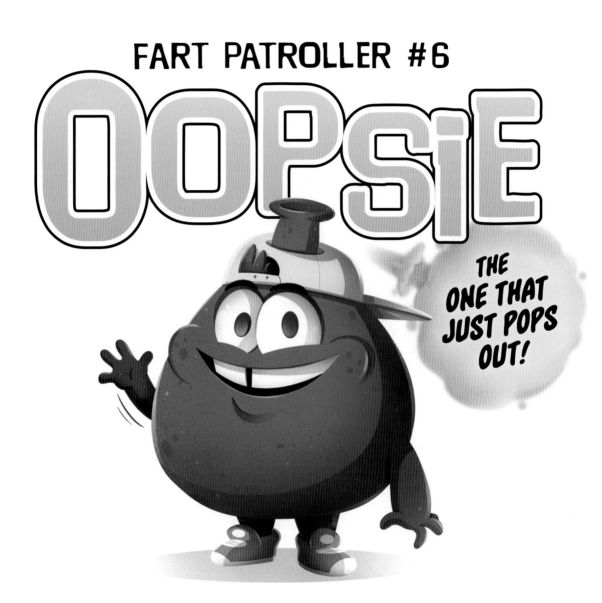

It's **OOPSIE** here, and it's time for fun,

Because I won't stop until I'm done

With giving human "beans" a **FRIGHT**

When I let loose about butt height.

That's right—those times you think you farted,

In fact you've simply been outsmarted

By little ol' me who's made you think

You've popped out an accidental ***STINK***!

Not that they're always all that **BAD**

(For which you really should be glad),

But smell of **ROTTEN** lemon skin

And moldy apples in the bin.

Like, it's not as if I mean you harm,

Or want to cause too much alarm,

But being on **FART PATROL** takes skill

And when I ... "oops!"... it's such a thrill.

So when I feel it's time to **POUNCE**,

I'll suck up air in large amounts,

And hold it in until it's *HOT*,

Then do some running on the spot.

I'll shut my eyes and **SPiN** around

And stamp my feet upon the ground,

Then

WheeeeEEP!

       I'll open up my spout

And let a real rip-snorter out!

School classrooms can be lots of fun

To **TEASE** young humans—one by one.

I'll hide beneath them when they sit

And let them settle down a bit,

Then **FART**, so very loud and clear

It reaches every student's ear,

And thirty kids will point and **STARE**

At my poor target sitting there.

"Oh please!" they'll groan. "Hey stop it, dude!"

"Hey Miss, Sebastian's being **RUDE**!"

"Oh **YUCK**!" the girls will shriek. "You beast,

You could have left the room at least!"

"Can we go home? Right now?" they'll croak.

"If we stay here, we're gonna choke!"

And on they'll go and cause him **SHAME**

Despite the fact he's not to blame!

I also like to play my **TRICKS**

On those the teacher always picks

As Best in Class, or Homework Star

(You know how clever some kids are).

I'll **SNEAK** up as he gets his prize,

And give them both a big surprise

By going

WheeeeEEP!

with such intent,

He's purple with ***EMBARRASSMENT***!

I also seek out Heads of Schools

(You know—the ones who make the rules,

And like to think they're oh so smart,

But sometimes can be **COLD** of heart).

I'll find one as he's standing tall,

At school in the assembly hall,

And listen to him as he **SCOLDS**

A kid who's not done as she's told.

I'll start to **SPiN** and gather speed,

And stamp my feet and then proceed

To let one loose as he declares:

"One week's detention—stacking chairs."

My

WheeeeEEp!

                will make him jump in **FRiGHT**,

And mutter words most impolite.

"Oops, what was that?" the kid will **YELL**,

"Now you should stack some chairs as well!"

My human will protest in vain

And wonder if he's gone **INSANE**.

"It wasn't me, dear girl," he'll whine,

"I am the Head, it can't be mine!"

So then I'll do another one

To make him really come undone,

And half the school will yell "*YAHOO*!"

As he's brought down a peg or two.

Oh yeah, I love the jokes I play

And the **PECULIAR** smells I lay,

And I'm particularly proud

When I can get them nice and **LOUD**.

It's such a hoot to make you sweat

And get all **NERVOUS** and upset,

In fact, the party's just begun

When I decide to have some fun!